Clare Young is a 40-year-old married mother of two girls from Lancashire. Clare has had a love of reading and writing from a young age and this is her first children's book. The idea came for the book from her two girls always moaning at bathtime and they having their hair washed, a concept many parents are familiar with. In her spare time, Clare loves music, meditation, exercise and being out in nature but more than anything its having fun and making memories. Clare loves sharing her stories, making children laugh and happy and putting a smile on the faces of people she meets and if she achieves that theirs nothing better. Her motto is that life is too short so enjoy, love, laugh, and just have fun fun fun.

STINKY STELLA'S
Amazing Bathroom Experience

CLARE YOUNG

Austin Macauley Publishers™
LONDON • CAMBRIDGE • NEW YORK • SHARJAH

A CIP catalogue record for this title is available from the British Library.

ISBN 9781398444515 (Paperback)
ISBN 9781398444522 (ePub e-book)

www.austinmacauley.com

First Published 2022
Austin Macauley Publishers Ltd®
1 Canada Square
Canary Wharf
London
E14 5AA

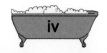

I would like to thank everyone (you know who you are) for taking the time out to read my work, giving ideas, and feedback. I really appreciate it. And lastly, I couldn't have done this without the support and belief of my husband, Anthony, and my two miracles, Amelia and Eve, love you all so much, you're amazing and thank you.

I would like to thank Austin Macauley Publishers for giving me the opportunity to see my book in print and putting it out there for the world to see. Thank you so much!

v

My sister stinks, I mean hold your nose and
hold your breath, you will absolutely gag,
that's no lie.

People run for their lives, friends don't come to play and do you know, even the bathroom is scared of her stench.

Stella hasn't had a bath in years and when she walks upstairs, the bathroom shakes in fear.

"Oh no," it says, "Stella's on her way in here."

Mum and Dad always shout, "Please, Stella, have a bath." But the answer is always, "Nooooooooooooo."

I want to tell you about this wonderful day,
when we are going far far away on our
family holiday.

We are ready to go with our bags packed
and pegs on our noses, really wishing Stella
would smell somewhat pleasant
for a change.

Dad shouts, "It's holiday time, let's go, go, go." We all shriek and shout with happiness. When what should happen, suddenly the car jerks, it spits, it splutters, all the windows and doors fly open, now it won't start.

"Oh great," says Dad, annoyed the car won't start, even the car can't stand the smell.

I look over at Stella, whose eyes were filling up with tears, her lips were quivering with sadness.

All of a sudden, she let out an almighty wail, "THAT'S IT, I WANT MY HOLIDAY NOOOOOOWWWWWWW!!"

Stella jumped out of the car and ran upstairs, followed by Mum, Dad and I, in amazement.

Stella paused at the bathroom door and said the words we were longing to hear, "I am going to have a bath."

Meanwhile inside the bathroom the bath, toilet and sink were frozen in shock, when suddenly the sink pipes up, "At least we don't have noses."

The toilet winks at the bath and says, "She will just make the taps water instead." And they all burst into laughter.

Stella stepped into the bathtub, and washed away years of dirt and grime. In fact she loved the bath so much, she was in there for hours.

Now I know what you're thinking, what about the holiday? Well, I'll tell you what happened next.

Mum, Dad and I were so bored outside waiting around for Stella, when we went in to see what was taking so long.

Stella was laying in the bath, fully clothed, stating she was never leaving the bathtub ever.

Mum said, "While I'm glad you're clean, Stella, really glad, what are we going to do about our holiday? How do we get there for a start?"

Everything went extremely quiet while we all thought about this. Then unexpectedly, the windows flew wide open.

Dad, in shock, sat on the toilet, which then
by surprise lifted off the ground and up
towards the window.

"What's happening?" shouted Dad, terrified,
clinging on for dear life.

The bathtub whizzed out after, with Stella
shrieking inside, and Mum and I held onto
the sink, laughing as we zoomed out of sight.

The bathroom, so nicely, took us on our holiday, but believe me, it was a ride none of us will forget in a hurry. But at least we are here now, alive and well.

Let's enjoy our holiday. Oh wait, hang on a second! Who has brought our cases? Nooooooooooooooooooooo!

The End!